SUPER STORM

by

ROGER HURN AND JANE A.C. WEST

Illustrated by Stik

To Pam – for giving shelter when the
storm comes.

With special thanks to:

Daniel Chambers
Paula Kirby
Aisha Pervaiz
Daniel Sinclair

First published in 2011 in Great Britain by
Barrington Stoke Ltd
18 Walker St, Edinburgh, EH3 7LP

www.barringtonstoke.co.uk

Copyright © 2011 Roger Hurn and Jane A. C. West
Illustrations © Stik

The moral right of the author has been asserted in
accordance with the Copyright, Designs and
Patents Act 1988

ISBN: 978-1-84299-600-3

Printed in China by Leo

The publisher gratefully acknowledges support from the Scottish Arts
Council towards the publication of this title.

WHO ARE TRIBE?

ARE THEY HUMANS?

OR ARE THEY ANIMALS?

Tribe are humans *and* animals.

They are super-heroes with special powers.

They can *shape-shift* – change from animals to humans and back again.

THEIR PLAN: to save the world from anyone who tries to destroy it.

Tribe need to find the bad guys – before it's too late.

The Earth is in trouble – and only Tribe have the power to help.

Tribe are helped by TOK – the Tree Of Knowledge.

Tribe can travel all over the world using the roots of trees.

Tribe also have the power to talk to animals – and they can send each other mind-messages, even when they are miles apart.

CAST LIST

Finn

Bruin

Kat

Mo

Talon

Vana

and ...

Dr Hed Case!

Contents

Chapter 1
News Flash

Tribe were in their Head Quarters – a tree-house in a huge oak tree, the Tree Of Knowledge, TOK. A news flash came on the Sap Screen.

Dr Hed Case, a mad scientist, wants 20 million pounds by midnight or he will set off a Super Storm that will destroy London!

Bruin said, "This guy Hed Case sounds like a real nut job. How can he set off a Super Storm?"

Kat hissed at him, "He's invented a machine that can control the weather – that's how!"

"It doesn't matter how he does it," said Vana. "How do we stop him?"

Tribe had to put an end to Dr Hed Case's evil plan. But first they had to find him.

Mo's eyes lit up. "I think he must be in a ship out in the North Sea."

"Why do you think that?" asked Vana.

Mo gave a shy smile. She didn't like to show off. "He'll have to send the Super Storm up the River Thames if he's going to destroy London," she said. "And the River Thames flows into the North Sea."

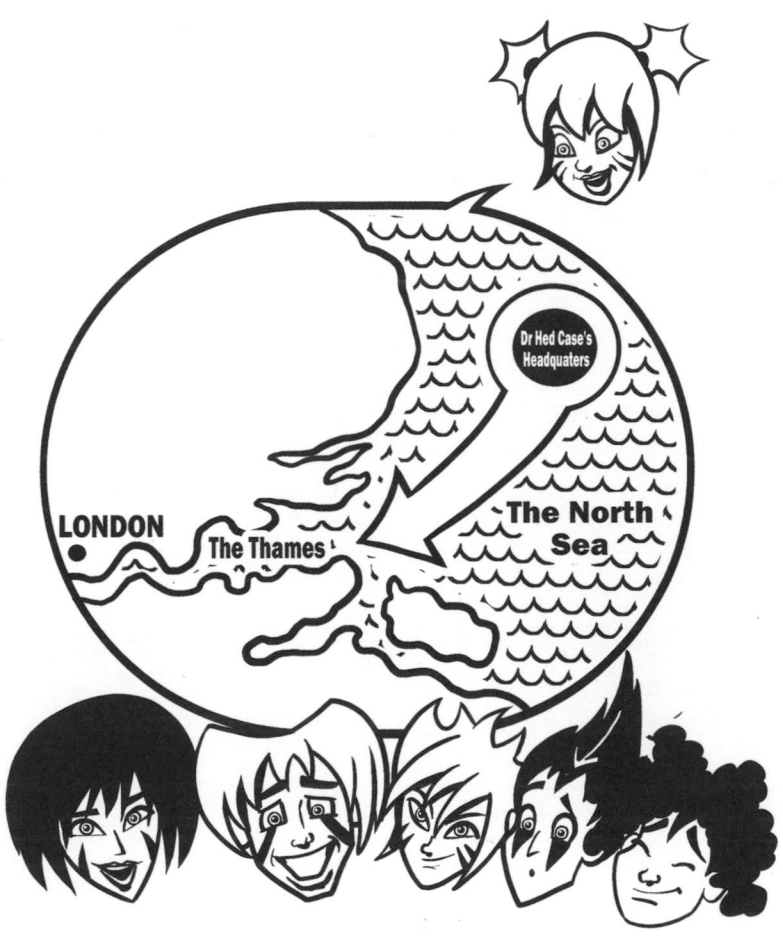

"You're right!" Vana punched the air. Then she growled. "Grrrr ... this is no job for me. I can't fly there."

"Or me," said Kat. "Cats hate water."

Finn jumped up and down. "I love water. And there are lots of dolphins in the North Sea. I bet they can help me track down Dr Hed Case."

The others agreed – but only if Talon went with him. Finn groaned. "But you can't swim, Talon."

"No, but my eagle eyes can see trouble coming a mile away," said Talon.

Vana nodded. "You'd better find Dr Hed Case by midnight or we'll *all* be up to our eyes in it!"

Chapter 2
Swimming with Dolphins

The North Sea was grey, choppy and cold but Finn didn't care. In fact he loved it. He was moving through the waves like a torpedo.

Talon soared high above the sea. His eagle eyes were sharp and alert. He was looking for Dr Hed Case's secret Head Quarters. But the sea was empty.

"That crazy doctor must be out here somewhere," he said to himself. "Why can't we find him?"

Finn saw a pod of dolphins leaping out of the water up ahead. He swam over to them. He wanted to join in with their jumping and diving games. But there was no time for fun now.

"Have you guys seen a nutty scientist in a boat?" he asked the dolphins. "He's got a storm machine."

The dolphin leader blew air out through her blow-hole with a loud snort. "We *have* seen him – but he doesn't live in a boat."

Finn smacked his tail down hard on the water. "What? That can't be right. Dr Hed Case is a man, not a fish. He can't live in the sea."

The dolphins all chirped happily, "He doesn't live in the sea. He lives in the old fort on Shivering Sands."

Finn felt excited. At last he was getting somewhere. "Where is that?"

The dolphin pointed with her flipper. "Shivering Sands is just out of sight over there, beyond the horizon. But it's a bad place. Storms rage over it night and day.

Keep away or you'll be in trouble!"

"No chance," said Finn. "It's Dr Hed Case who'll be in trouble now – not me!"

Chapter 3
Shivering Sands

Shivering Sands was a spooky place. The fort rose up out of the sea like a huge concrete spider with metal legs. Dark clouds filled the sky above it. Thunder boomed.

Talon swooped down from the sky, close to Finn. "Do you think this is Dr Hed Case's hide-out?"

Finn nodded. "It looks spooky enough and the weather's so weird it's giving me goose bumps. Why don't you go and check it out?"

Talon flew up to the window at the top of the fort's control tower. He perched on the window sill and peeked in. A man with wild hair was hunched up over a weird metal machine. Bright yellow sparks flew out of it, and it made a noise like a million football fans all screaming at the same time. It was Dr Hed Case's Super Storm Maker!

Talon flew back down to Finn. "It's him. He's cooking up a huge storm in his machine. It'll be ready to blow any time now. We have to do something before it's too late! Come on!"

Chapter 4
The Countdown Begins

Talon and Finn morphed back into their human shapes and climbed up the rusty iron ladder on the side of the control tower. They stood on the platform outside the control room door.

"We'll kick open the door and dash inside," said Talon. "Ready?"

Finn nodded.

Talon grabbed the door handle. "Let's go!"

The two boys burst into the room. Dr Hed Case jumped as if he'd been poked in the bottom with a sharp stick. "Who are you?" he snarled.

"We're Tribe and we're here to stop your evil plan to flood London."

The crazy scientist giggled. "Hee hee! Do you two twits think you can stop a genius like me? I'm going to show no pity to London City!"

"But think about all the people who will die!" Talon said.

Dr Hed Case sneered. "Who cares about them? I wanted my 20 million pounds!"

Talon and Finn felt fear like a cold hand twisting in their guts.

"He's going to do it," said Finn.

"Yes, I am." Dr Hed Case's voice was sharp and cold as a razor. "If I can't have the money, I'll make *everyone* pay!"

He reached out and turned a key that was sticking out from the Super Storm machine.

"Now I've begun the countdown. In 30 seconds, the Super Storm will be on its way to London. It will destroy everything in its path. London will vanish under a huge wave of water!"

Finn and Talon looked at each other in horror. Then Finn had an idea. "Hey, maybe we can just turn the machine off again!"

Finn ran across the room and tried to grab the key. But Dr Hed Case was too fast for him. He snatched the key from the machine and dropped it out of the window.

Chapter 5
Just in Time

Finn jumped out of the window after the key. The key hit the sea and vanished under the waves. There were only 20 seconds left to stop the storm.

Finn morphed as he fell and did a perfect dolphin dive. He swam down deep and grabbed the key in his mouth. With a flick of his tail he shot back up to the top. But now there were only 10 seconds left.

29

Talon was hovering in the air, waiting for him. He grabbed the key in his beak and flew back to the tower.

"Go, Talon," yelled Finn. "You've got to beat that countdown!"

Talon hurtled back in to the control room and changed back into a boy. There were 5 seconds left. He ran past Dr Case and put the key into the lock. There were only 2 seconds left.

But Talon didn't know which way to turn the key. He had one second left to make up his mind. He began to twist the key to the right. Then he saw Dr Hed Case's face reflected in the shiny metal surface of the machine. He had a nasty smile. This told Talon all he needed to know.

"Thanks for the heads up, Hed Case," he said. "Left it is."

He twisted the key to the left and held his breath. The machine shuddered, gave a groan and then stopped and fell silent. Talon had acted just in time!

Dr Hed Case jumped up and down in a rage. "You fool. Now the storm will blow up in here! You've saved London, but now you will die!" At once, Talon changed back into an eagle. He flew out of the window and up into the sky. Far below him the fort exploded. But Talon was safe!

Talon flew around looking for Finn. Had he made it? At last, he saw Finn swimming away from Shivering Sands. He zoomed down to him.

"Well done, Talon. You made it." Finn jumped out of the water and did a back flip. "But what happened to Dr Hed Case?"

"I don't know. I didn't see if he escaped from the fort before it blew up." Talon gave a loud screech. "But I've got a funny feeling we'll be meeting up with him again some day."

Finn blew a stream of bubbles. "I'll race you home. Last one back to the tree-house is a stinky squid!"

THAMES FLOOD RISKS RISE!

Global warming is a slow rise in the temperature of the Earth. Most scientists think it is happening because of things humans are doing. Unless we do something about the problem soon, it could change the planet for the worse.

Many kinds of animals and plants will become extinct and life will be much harder for everyone. The sea is rising because of global warming. That means that London could have floods!

The Thames Barrier is not strong enough to stop the kind of floods we could have.

Time is running out and we must act fast. To find out more about climate change, go to: http://tiki.oneworld.net/global_warming /climate_home.html.

FiNN – DOLPHiN BOY

SPECIAL SKILL: can use his dolphin sonar powers as a weapon.

LOVES: making a splash; wild places and stormy seas.

HATES: sharks, big fishing nets, polluted water.

MOST LIKELY TO SAY: "I won't be any trouble – honest!"

BIGGEST SECRET: doesn't know if he wants to be a dolphin or a human.

TRIBE TALK!

To: Finn

From: Katy

Subject: Global Warming

Dear Finn,

What can I do to help stop global warming?

Katy

TRIBE TALK!

To:	Katy
From:	Finn
Subject:	Re: Global Warming

Dear Katy,

You can help slow down global warming by turning off your TV, DVD player and computer when you're not using them. That's what I do.

Splish splash, gotta dash!

Finn

FYI: DOLPHINS

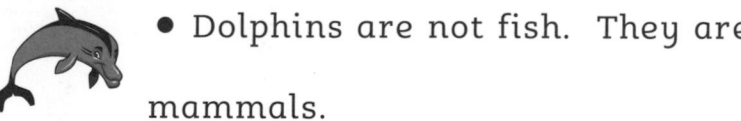
- Dolphins don't really smile, it's just the way their mouths are shaped!

- Dolphins are not fish. They are mammals.

- Dolphins come to the top of the water to breathe.

 • Dolphins can hold their breath for several minutes and can dive down to depths of over 300m.

 • Dolphins like to eat herring, mackerel and sardines.

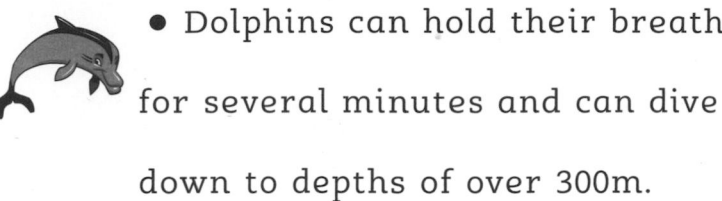 • An adult dolphin can eat up to 30kg of food a day.

30kg

JOKE OF THE DAY

FINN: What makes a bigger splash than a jumping dolphin?

TALON: I don't know...

FINN: Two jumping dolphins!

CHECK OUT THE REST OF
THE TRIBE BOOKS!

For more info check out our website:
www.barringtonstoke.co.uk